The Old Fashioned Mental Arithmetic Book

The no-nonsense book
of practice in
mental arithmetic
(with answers)

 Ward Lock Educational Co. Ltd.

WARD LOCK EDUCATIONAL CO. LTD.
1 CHRISTOPHER ROAD
EAST GRINSTEAD
SUSSEX RH19 3BT
UNITED KINGDOM

A MEMBER OF THE LING KEE GROUP
HONG KONG · SINGAPORE · LONDON · NEW YORK

Text © Toni Tourret

First published – 1982
Reprinted – 1982, 1992 (twice), 1993

ISBN 0-7062-4160-6

Note to the reader
Pencil in your answers lightly so that you can rub
them out and practise again. You can check your
answers at the back of the book.

Other titles in this series:
The Old Fashioned Rules of Punctutation Book
ISBN 0 7062 4123 1
The Old Fashioned Rules of Grammar Book
ISBN 0 7062 3850 8
The Old Fashioned Rules of Spelling Book
ISBN 0 7062 4085 5
The Old Fashioned Handwriting Book
ISBN 0 7062 4139 8
The Old Fashioned Multiplication Book
ISBN 0 7062 4121 5
The Old Fashioned Division Book
ISBN 0 7062 4122 3
The Old Fashioned Adding-Up Book
ISBN 0 7062 4086 3
The Old Fashioned Taking-Away Book
ISBN 0 7062 4148 7
The Old Fashioned Times Table Book
ISBN 0 7062 3749 8

Printed in Hong Kong

Adding up units

Look at these adding sums. The units together add up to ten and some units. Add the second number in stages.

So to do $7 + 5$, add the 5 in two stages, 3 then 2:

$$7 \xrightarrow{+3} 10 \xrightarrow{+2} \underline{12}$$

Here are some more examples:

$7 + 7$: $\qquad 7 \xrightarrow{+3} 10 \xrightarrow{+4} \underline{14}$

$8 + 9$: $\qquad 8 \xrightarrow{+2} 10 \xrightarrow{+7} \underline{17}$

$6 + 9$: $\qquad 6 \xrightarrow{+4} 10 \xrightarrow{+5} \underline{15}$

Try adding these quickly in your head:

1. $8 + 7 =$

2. $9 + 3 =$

3. $5 + 8 =$

4. $6 + 7 =$

5. $6 + 8 =$

6. $9 + 4 =$

7. $7 + 4 =$

8. $5 + 9 =$

9. $3 + 8 =$

10. $9 + 9 =$

11. $5 + 6 =$

12. $8 + 8 =$

Adding units to numbers greater than ten

Now let's practise adding units to numbers greater than ten. First add up to the next ten, then add on the remaining units.

So to do 15 + 7 work in two stages:

$$15 \xrightarrow{+5} 20 \xrightarrow{+2} \underline{22}$$

To do 26 + 8 : $26 \xrightarrow{+4} 30 \xrightarrow{+4} \underline{34}$

To do 35 + 9 : $35 \xrightarrow{+5} 40 \xrightarrow{+4} \underline{44}$

Add these in your head:

1. 18 + 4 =

2. 28 + 4 =

3. 14 + 7 =

4. 24 + 7 =

5. 15 + 9 =

6. 23 + 9 =

7. 28 + 8 =

8. 39 + 7 =

9. 41 + 9 =

10. 26 + 7 =

11. 43 + 8 =

12. 34 + 9 =

13. 55 + 6 =

14. 58 + 7 =

Adding on tens

Look at these adding sums. Add the numbers in the tens position. The units stay the same.

To do 15 + 10 : $15 \xrightarrow{+10} \underline{25}$

To do 26 + 20 : $26 \xrightarrow{+20} \underline{46}$

Add these quickly in your head:

1. 7 + 10 =

2. 14 + 10 =

3. 8 + 20 =

4. 28 + 20 =

5. 14 + 20 =

6. 15 + 30 =

7. 26 + 30 =

8. 45 + 30 =

9. 23 + 50 =

10. 33 + 40 =

11. 38 + 20 =

12. 39 + 20 =

13. 48 + 30 =

14. 57 + 20 =

15. 22 + 40 =

Check your answers. If you can add on tens easily, turn over. If you want to improve your speed, do them again.

Adding together numbers with tens and units

Adding numbers with both tens and units is easy if it is done in stages.

Here are two ways to do 35 + 27:

either $\qquad 35 \xrightarrow{+7} 42 \xrightarrow{+20} \underline{62}$

or $\qquad 35 \xrightarrow{+20} 55 \xrightarrow{+7} \underline{62}$

Practise with these:

1.   43 + 18 =

2.   29 + 26 =

3.   45 + 28 =

4.   57 + 39 =

5.   32 + 58 =

6.   39 + 44 =

7.   65 + 25 =

8.   84 + 14 =

9.   29 + 66 =

10.   17 + 59 =

11.   64 + 17 =

12.   36 + 29 =

13.   44 + 37 =

14.   49 + 23 =

Check your answers. If they were all correct, well done. If not, perhaps you need to practise the previous pages again.

Taking away

Look at these taking away or subtraction sums. You can do subtraction by counting on from the smaller number, to see how much you need to add to get to the larger number.

So to do 15 − 9 work in stages, counting on to ten first

$$9 \rightarrow 10 \rightarrow 15$$
$$1 + 5 = \underline{6}$$

To do 18 − 7 : $7 \rightarrow 10 \rightarrow 18$
$$3 + 8 = \underline{11}$$

Practise with these:

1. 17 − 8 =

2. 15 − 7 =

3. 14 − 5 =

4. 18 − 9 =

5. 13 − 6 =

6. 19 − 9 =

7. 12 − 8 =

8. 14 − 9 =

9. 15 − 4 =

10. 13 − 4 =

11. 17 − 9 =

12. 15 − 8 =

13. 12 − 7 =

14. 12 − 4 =

Taking away tens

Now let's practise taking away tens.

To do 47 − 20, count on from 20 in two stages:

$$20 \to 40 \to 47$$
$$20 + 7 = \underline{27}$$

To do 39 − 10 : $10 \to 30 \to 39$
$$20 + 9 = \underline{29}$$

Practise with these:

1.   27 − 20 =

2.   48 − 30 =

3.   39 − 10 =

4.   26 − 10 =

5.   38 − 30 =

6.   55 − 40 =

7.   67 − 30 =

8.   44 − 20 =

9.   36 − 10 =

10.   43 − 20 =

11.   47 − 30 =

12.   41 − 20 =

13.   66 − 40 =

14.   28 − 10 =

15.   69 − 40 =

Check your answers. Turn over if you were fast and accurate.

6

Taking away tens and units

Taking away tens and units is easy if it is done in stages.

To do 35 − 17, count on from 17 to the next ten first:

$$17 \rightarrow 20 \rightarrow 35$$
$$3 + 15 = \underline{18}$$

To do 53 − 28 : $28 \rightarrow 30 \rightarrow 53$
$$2 + 23 = \underline{25}$$

Practise with these:

1. 37 − 19 =

2. 46 − 28 =

3. 54 − 18 =

4. 56 − 37 =

5. 43 − 25 =

6. 67 − 38 =

7. 42 − 15 =

8. 41 − 27 =

9. 72 − 47 =

0. 85 − 58 =

1. 63 − 45 =

2. 54 − 36 =

3. 48 − 32 =

4. 81 − 63 =

5. 77 − 58 =

Multiplying

Here are some multiplying sums. *Use* the times tables. To work fast, you will need to know your times tables forwards and backwards.

$$6 \times 7 = 7 \times 6 = \underline{42}$$

$$8 \times 3 = 3 \times 8 = \underline{24}$$

Answer these quickly:

1. $6 \times 4 =$

2. $7 \times 8 =$

3. $5 \times 5 =$

4. $6 \times 6 =$

5. $8 \times 9 =$

6. $7 \times 7 =$

7. $9 \times 7 =$

8. $6 \times 8 =$

9. $5 \times 7 =$

10. $4 \times 9 =$

11. $7 \times 4 =$

12. $4 \times 6 =$

13. $5 \times 8 =$

14. $7 \times 3 =$

15. $8 \times 8 =$

Check your answers. If you worked fast and got them all right, well done. If you need to improve, remember that practice makes perfect.

Dividing

The times tables can also be used for division. If you know your times tables backwards and forwards, you will know the answer straight away to any simple division question.

The numbers 7, 8 and 56 give you four facts you can use:

$$7 \times 8 = \underline{56} \qquad 56 \div 7 = \underline{8}$$

$$8 \times 7 = \underline{56} \qquad 56 \div 8 = \underline{7}$$

And for 4, 6 and 24:

$$4 \times 6 = \underline{24} \qquad 24 \div 6 = \underline{4}$$

$$6 \times 4 = \underline{24} \qquad 24 \div 4 = \underline{6}$$

Now answer these quickly:

1. $42 \div 6 =$

2. $64 \div 8 =$

3. $49 \div 7 =$

4. $48 \div 8 =$

5. $54 \div 9 =$

6. $45 \div 5 =$

7. $32 \div 4 =$

8. $36 \div 6 =$

9. $63 \div 7 =$

10. $72 \div 8 =$

11. $21 \div 3 =$

Check your answers. If they were all right, well done. If you want to improve your speed, do them again.

A mental arithmetic test

1. 42 + 20 =

2. 37 − 24 =

3. 56 ÷ 8 =

4. 7 × 9 =

5. 38 + 27 =

6. 27 − 19 =

7. 64 ÷ 8 =

8. 5 × 7 =

9. 72 + 19 =

0. 43 − 25 =

1. 36 ÷ 6 =

2. 8 × 4 =

3. 29 + 36 =

4. 45 − 29 =

5. 28 ÷ 7 =

6. 9 × 8 =

7. 49 + 23 =

8. 34 − 18 =

9. 32 ÷ 4 =

0. 7 × 7 =

Check your answers. Well done. You
have now finished the book.

Answers

Page 1
1. 15 2. 12 3. 13 4. 13 5. 14 6. 13 7. 11 8. 14 9. 11 10. 18
11. 11 12. 16

Page 2
1. 22 2. 32 3. 21 4. 31 5. 24 6. 32 7. 36 8. 46 9. 50 10. 33
11. 51 12. 43 13. 61 14. 65

Page 3
1. 17 2. 24 3. 28 4. 48 5. 34 6. 45 7. 56 8. 75 9. 73 10. 73
11. 58 12. 59 13. 78 14. 77 15. 62

Page 4
1. 61 2. 55 3. 73 4. 96 5. 90 6. 83 7. 90 8. 98 9. 95 10. 76
11. 81 12. 65 13. 81 14. 72

Page 5
1. 9 2. 8 3. 9 4. 9 5. 7 6. 10 7. 4 8. 5 9. 11 10. 9 11. 8
12. 7 13. 5 14. 8

Page 6
1. 7 2. 18 3. 29 4. 16 5. 8 6. 15 7. 37 8. 24 9. 26 10. 23
11. 17 12. 21 13. 26 14. 18 15. 29

Page 7
1. 18 2. 18 3. 36 4. 19 5. 18 6. 29 7. 27 8. 14 9. 25 10. 27
11. 18 12. 18 13. 16 14. 18 15. 19

Page 8
1. 24 2. 56 3. 25 4. 36 5. 72 6. 49 7. 63 8. 48 9. 35 10. 36
11. 28 12. 24 13. 40 14. 21 15. 64

Page 9
1. 7 2. 8 3. 7 4. 6 5. 6 6. 9 7. 8 8. 6 9. 9 10. 9 11. 7

Page 10
1. 62 2. 13 3. 7 4. 63 5. 65 6. 8 7. 8 8. 35 9. 91 10. 18
11. 6 12. 32 13. 65 14. 16 15. 4 16. 72 17. 72 18. 16 19. 8 20. 49